Comprehensi Book 1

C000285534

CONTENTS

UNIT 1

A letter from Sarah

Sarah has just moved to a new house
a long way from her best friend.

1 White Road,
Sunnyside,
Devon, EX8 2EY

Saturday, 7th June

Dear Jane,

How are you? It is quite nice here but I do miss all my friends. My new school is all right but I don't know many people yet.

I have made a den in the garden. I am not going to let Sam and Anna in unless they know the password. The password is "starfish".

Our house is very close to the beach. The beach is sandy. There are rock pools at the far end. I found a crab in one. Dad says he will buy me a fishing net. We can use it when you come. I am glad you are coming to stay with us. I can't wait.

Sam likes his new playgroup and Anna is going to start in September when she is three.

That is all my news. Please write soon.

Love from,

Sarah

Answer in sentences. Some of the answers have been started for you. *(3 marks each)*

1   What did Sarah find in the rock pool?
    Sarah found a ...

2   How old is Sarah's sister, Anna?
    Anna is ...

3   What is the password to Sarah's den?
    The password is ...

4   Is the beach sandy or stony?

5   How can you tell that Sarah is older than Sam and Anna?

3

UNIT 2

How to make a melon seed necklace

You can make a necklace from melon seeds.

What to do:

1

2

3

4

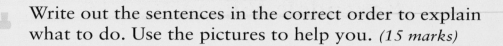

Write out the sentences in the correct order to explain what to do. Use the pictures to help you. *(15 marks)*

Wash the seeds and spread them on a towel to dry.

When your necklace is long enough, tie the two ends of cotton together.

Thread a needle with a long piece of cotton and make a big knot at the end.

Push the needle and cotton through the end of each seed.

Baxendale Village

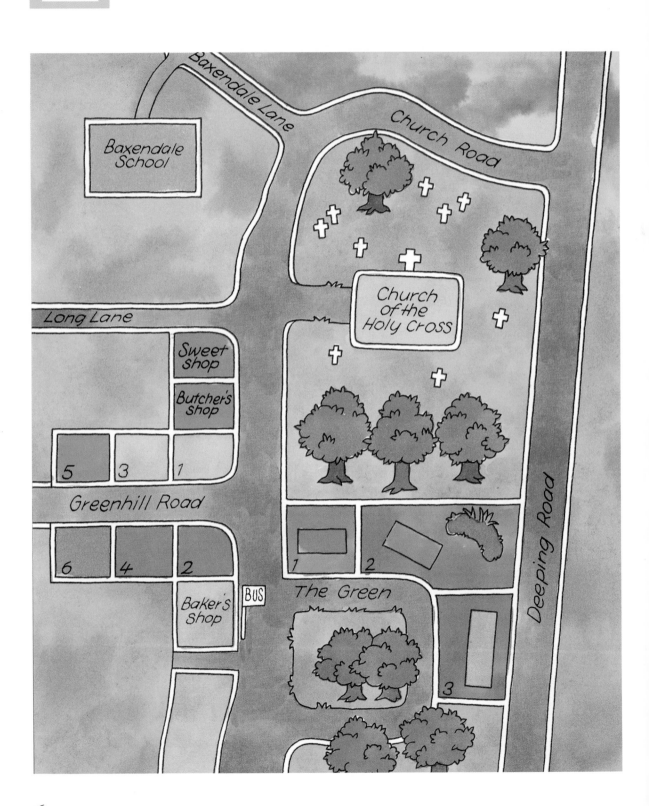

Choose the correct answer to each question and write it out.

1   Is there a sweet shop in Baxendale Village? *(1 mark)*

   a) No, there is not a sweet shop.
   b) Yes, there is a sweet shop.

2   Which house has a pond in the garden? *(2 marks)*

   a) 3 The Green has a pond in the garden.
   b) 2 The Green has a pond in the garden.

3   Which house is next door to 5 Greenhill Road? *(2 marks)*

   a) 6 Greenhill Road is next door to 5 Greenhill Road.
   b) 3 Greenhill Road is next door to 5 Greenhill Road.

4   How many trees are there in the churchyard? *(2 marks)*

   a) There are five trees in the churchyard.
   b) There are three trees in the churchyard.

5   Where does the bus stop in Baxendale? *(2 marks)*

   a) The bus stops by the church.
   b) The bus stops by the baker's shop.

6   What is the name of the church in Baxendale Village? *(2 marks)*

   a) The church is called the Church of the Holy Cross.
   b) The church is called Baxendale Church.

7   Which road is Baxendale School on? *(2 marks)*

   a) Baxendale School is on Long Lane.
   b) Baxendale School is on Baxendale Lane.

8   How many houses are there on The Green? *(2 marks)*

   a) There are two houses on The Green.
   b) There are three houses on The Green.

The holiday club

Join the

MANOR FARM HOLIDAY CLUB!

It costs just £5 to join,
and then 50p each time you come.
Fun and games every day of the summer holidays!
mornings: 5-8 years
afternoons: 9-11 years

**Swimming Pony rides
Table-tennis Painting
Kite-making Computers
Model-making Cooking
Bouncy Castle**

Find out more from:
Mrs Green, Manor Farm, Old Road, Deeping.
Telephone: 821 0238

1   Ben wants to join the holiday club.
    How much does it cost to join?

    It costs ...

2   Ben is seven years old. Will he go in the mornings or the afternoons?

    Ben will go to the club in the ...

3   How much will he pay each time he goes to the club?

    He will pay ...

4   Can he make a kite at the club?

5   How can Ben find out more about the club?
    Write down two things that he could do.

UNIT 5

Brachiosaurus

This is how you say it -
brack-ee-oh-SAW-russ.

This dinosaur was fat. It was too fat to run from enemies.
That is why it stayed in the water. It was safe there, and
food was close by. It ate plants.

Peggy Parrish from *Dinosaur Time* (Harper Collins)

 Answer in sentences. Some of the answers have been
started for you. *(3 marks each)*

1   What kind of food did the brachiosaurus eat?
   The brachiosaurus ate ...

2   Why couldn't the brachiosaurus run very fast?
   It couldn't run very fast because ...

3   Where did the brachiosaurus stay to be safe?
   The brachiosaurus stayed ...

4   What word is the opposite of "enemies"?
   The opposite of "enemies" is ...

5   What word is the opposite of "safe"?

One dark night

Late one night, Mittens was feeling
bored. She looked across at Hannah,
her friend, who was fast asleep on a
chair in the kitchen. Their owners
had shut them in before they went
to bed. But Mittens noticed they had
forgotten to shut the cat-flap. She
suddenly felt excited at the thought
of the dark garden. She would go out!
She would see what it was like at night!

Rebecca Taylor from *The Kitnapping of Mittens* (Puffin Books)

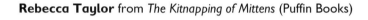

Read about Mittens and then answer
the questions. *(3 marks each)*

1 Write down the sentence that is true.

   a) Mittens was asleep on a chair.
   b) Mittens had a friend called Hannah.

2 Write out the sentence and fill in the missing word.

   Mittens was _____ when she thought about going outside.

3 Copy and finish this sentence.

   Mittens got out into the garden through the _____

4 Look at the picture of the book about Mittens.
   What do you think will happen to her when she goes out
   into the garden?

5 Look at the picture of Mittens.
   Why do you think she is called Mittens?

U N I T

7

Invisible ink

Lemon juice makes good invisible ink.
This is what you have to do.

1

Ask a grown-up to cut a lemon
in half. Squeeze the juice into a
small bowl.

2

Dip a small stick into the juice
and write a message with it on
some white paper.

3

Wait for the paper to dry.
Your message will now be
invisible.

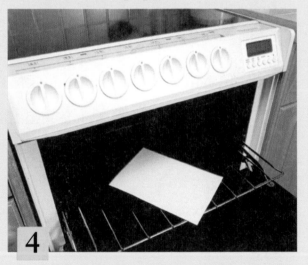

4

Hold the message near a warm
lamp bulb (or ask a grown-up
to put it in a warm oven for a
few minutes) and your message
will appear.

Write out the sentences and fill in the
missing words. *(3 marks each)*

1 "Invisible" means that you cannot _____ something.

2 You should ask a grown-up to _____ the lemon.

3 Write with a _____ instead of a pen.

4 The message becomes invisible when the paper is completely
_____ .

5 The writing will appear when you leave the paper in a
_____ place.

Mog the forgetful cat

Once there was a cat called Mog and she lived with a family called Thomas. Mog was nice but not very clever. She didn't understand a lot of things. A lot of other things she forgot. She was a very forgetful cat.

Sometimes she ate her supper. Then she forgot that she'd eaten it.

Sometimes she thought of something in the middle of washing her leg. Then she forgot to wash the rest of it.

Once she forgot that cats can't fly.

But most of all she forgot her cat flap. The cat flap led from the kitchen into the garden. Mog could go out ... and in again. It was her own little door.

The garden always made Mog very excited. She smelled all the smells. She chased the birds. She climbed the trees. She ran round and round with a big fluffed-up tail. And then she forgot the cat flap. She forgot that she had a cat flap. She wanted to go back into the house, but she couldn't remember how.

Judith Kerr from *Mog the Forgetful Cat* (Harper Collins)

Answer in sentences.
Some of the answers have been started for you.

1   What was the name of the family Mog lived with? *(2 marks)*
The name of Mog's family was …

2   What things did Mog forget?
Write down all the things you can find. *(5 marks)*
Mog forgot that …

3   How did Mog get in and out of the house? *(2 marks)*

4   Write down three things Mog did in the garden. *(3 marks)*

5   Why couldn't Mog go back inside the house? *(3 marks)*

The boy and the lion

Once there was a boy who worked for a king. But the king was cruel to him. So the boy ran away. He met a big lion in the desert. The boy was afraid because the lion looked angry.

The lion said, "I am angry because there is a thorn in my foot." So the boy sat down and pulled the thorn out. The boy and the lion became good friends.

One day the boy went back to the town. That day the cruel king went hunting in the desert and he caught the lion in a net. Then he saw the boy in the town and he caught him as well.

"I will punish you for running away. I will throw you to the lion," said the king. So the king threw the boy into the lion's den. But when the lion saw the boy, he lay down and smiled. The boy smiled too and put his arm around his friend. The king was amazed and he let the boy and the lion go free.

Val Biro retold in *Fables of Aesop* (Ginn & Co)

 Answer in sentences. *(3 marks each)*

1 Why did the boy run away from the king?

2 How did the boy help the lion?

3 How did the king punish the boy when he caught him?

4 What did the lion do when he saw the boy?

5 Why did the king let the boy and the lion go free?

Hiccup Harry

Do you know what a hiccup is?

HIC! HIC! HIC!

This is the story of the worst hiccups I ever had. Every kid in my school had to stop work because of them. It happened when I was (HIC!) years old! Six years old, I mean.

The hiccups began when we were sitting cross-legged on the carpet in the book corner. Mrs Hobbs was calling the register.

"Tracey?"

"Here, Miss."

"Bernard?"

"Here, Miss."

"Sharon?"

"Here, Miss."

"Harry?"

"Hic!"

"What was that, Harry?"

"HIC!"

"He's got hiccups, Miss," said Sharon.

Answer in sentences.
(3 marks each)

1 Where were the children sitting when the register was called?

2 What was the teacher's name?

3 Who told the teacher that Harry had hiccups?

4 What word is used to show the sound that Harry made?

5 Harry says that every "kid" in his school had to stop work because of his hiccups. What other word could he have used instead of "kid"?

Chris Powling and Scoular Anderson from *Hiccup Harry* (Penguin/Dutton USA)

U N I T

11

Special request

The day Mum had a record request on the radio
she was in the kitchen
putting the washing on.
We called her
and called her
and called her
but all she said was,
"Turn that radio down!
I can't hear what you're saying."
So we shouted again
as loud as we could
and in the end she came
just as the record was finishing.
"That's my favourite song,"
she said.
"Why didn't you call me?"
So we explained.
She's still not sure whether to believe us
or not.
"Me?" she said. "Me?
A record for me?"

Brian Morse from *All in the Family,* edited by
John Foster (Oxford University Press)

1 The record on the radio was asked for especially for
_____.

2 It was Mum's _____ song.

3 Mum was busy with the _____ when the record began.

4 Mum asked them to turn the radio down because she couldn't
_____ them.

5 When Mum came into the room, the record had almost
_____.

6 Mum could hardly _____ that the record was
especially for her.

UNIT 12

The sandcastle

It was the best sandcastle Joss had ever made.

He had built it high on the beach so the sea wouldn't wash it away.

Now his mum and dad were calling him and he could see they were the last family left on the beach.

"Good," said Joss. "Everyone has gone. Perhaps my castle will still be here in the morning."

Joss and his mum and dad were staying in a little house near the seaside. Joss looked out of the window. It was getting dark. He thought about his castle.

"Please let it still be there," he wished.

And it was. The next morning Joss and his mum and dad went down to the beach. They were the first family there.

"First on and last off," said Mum.

Joss found his castle easily. It hadn't crumbled or been trodden on by dogs. But something was different. He bent down and looked through the windows.

He could hear the sound of a trumpet. Suddenly he saw who was blowing it.

It was a little herald with his eyes wide open in fright.

Mary Hoffman from *King of the Castle* (Hamish Hamilton)

Answer in sentences.

1 How did Joss make sure that the sea would not wash his sandcastle away? *(2 marks)*

2 What else did Joss worry might happen to his sandcastle? *(4 marks)*

3 What did Joss hear when he bent down and looked through the windows of his sandcastle? *(2 marks)*

4 What did Joss's mother mean when she said, "First on, last off"? *(3 marks)*

5 Why was the little herald frightened? *(4 marks)*

UNIT 13

Pocket money

The twenty-five pupils in Class 2 are doing a project on pocket money. Everyone in the class has answered this question:

How much pocket money do you get each week?

None ☐ 10p ☐ 20p ☐ 30p ☐ 40p ☐ 50p ☐

more than 50p ☐

All the answers have been counted and Ben has made this list:

Number of children getting more than 50p a week: 3

Number of children getting 50p a week: 2

Number of children getting 40p a week: 3

Number of children getting 30p a week: 5

Number of children getting 20p a week: 6

Number of children getting 10p a week: 1

Number of children getting no pocket money: 5

Tom wanted to find out if other people had to do jobs at home to earn their pocket money. He has to help with the washing-up every day and he has to make his bed.
He thought they should ask:

Do you have to earn your pocket money by doing jobs?

Yes ☐   No ☐

Gemma said that she doesn't get pocket money but her mother often buys her sweets and her father buys her a comic every week. She thought they should ask:

Do you really need pocket money?

Yes ☐   No ☐

Answer the questions by writing out the sentences and filling in the missing words. *(3 marks each)*

1   How many children are there in Class 2?
There are _____ children in Class 2.

2   How many children in Class 2 don't get any pocket money?
_____ children don't get any pocket money.

3   How many children get 20 pence pocket money a week?
_____ children get 20 pence pocket money a week.

4   What jobs does Tom do at home to earn his pocket money?
Tom has to help with the _____ and he has to make _____.

5   What does Gemma's father buy her every week?
He buys her a _____ every week.

Harry's hamster

One day Harry was walking home from school with his friend, Ali.

They stopped to look in the window of the pet shop.

"Look, Ali!" said Harry. "Hamsters! Only one pound each!"

A small golden hamster sat up and looked at Harry through the shop window.

It twitched its whiskers and wiggled its nose.

It was the nicest hamster Harry had ever seen.

"I'm going to buy that hamster," he said. "On Saturday. When I get my pocket money."

Ali laughed.

"You've got a goldfish and a tortoise and a dog already," he said. "Your mum will go mad."

Harry shook his head.

"No, she won't," he said. "My mum likes hamsters."

On Saturday Harry's dad gave Harry his pocket money.

"Thanks, dad," said Harry. "I'm going to buy a hamster."

"Good grief!" said his dad. "You've got a goldfish and a tortoise and a big, daft dog already. What's your mum going to say?"

"It's all right, dad," smiled Harry. "Mum likes hamsters."

Harry and Ali and Dusty the dog ran down the street to the pet shop.

Harry looked in the window. The tiny hamster was still there. It wiggled its nose at Harry.

"Come on," said Harry, and in they went.

Sheila Lavelle from *Harry's Hamster* (Hamish Hamilton)

 Answer in sentences.

1   What was the name of Harry's friend? *(2 marks)*

2   How much did the hamster cost? *(2 marks)*

3   What colour was the hamster? *(2 marks)*

4   How did the hamster move its whiskers and nose? *(4 marks)*

5   What was the name of Harry's dog? *(2 marks)*

6   What do you think Harry's mother will say when he comes
     home with a hamster? *(3 marks)*

Mornings

If I wake up before it's dawn
And Mum is still asleep,
I sneak barefoot across the hall
To the kitchen where Bud sleeps.

I shush him if he makes a sound,
I tell him not to bark,
And then we creep back to my bed
And snuggle in the dark.

Then I go back to sleep again
With Bud right by my toes,
And wake to find him licking me
And touch his cold, round nose.

And when Mum's clock is ringing loud
And she yells out, "Wake up!"
I put the tea-bags in the pot,
Pour milk into our cups.

"Hello," she yawns, her work clothes on,
And Bud jumps up and down.
And then she laughs and fusses him,
Calls him a great big clown.

I like it in the mornings
Sitting drinking tea,
Watching the sky change colour,
Just Mum and Bud and me.

Michelle Magorian from *Waiting for My Shorts to Dry*
(Viking Kestrel)

⚷ **Answer in sentences.**

1   What was the name of the dog in the poem? *(2 marks)*

2   Where did the dog usually sleep? *(3 marks)*

3   Which word in Verse 1 means "creep secretly"? *(2 marks)*

4   Why couldn't Bud bark or make a sound in Verse 2? *(3 marks)*

5   Which of the following sentences is *not* true? Write it down. *(2 marks)*

      a) The child put the tea-bags in the teapot.
      b) The child poured the boiling water into the teapot.
      c) The child poured milk into Mum's cup.

6   What made Mum laugh and say that Bud was "a great big clown"? *(3 marks)*

27

Making bubbles

1

Stir four spoons of washing-up liquid into a small tumbler of water.

2

Use some thin wire to make a loop with a handle. Dip the loop into the mixture.

3

Make sure the loop is covered with the mixture.

4

Blow steadily through the loop. The mixture stretches around the air you blow out to make a bubble.

Rebecca Heddle from *Science in the Kitchen* (Usborne Publishing Ltd)

 Answer in sentences.

1 What do you mix together to make the bubble mixture? *(4 marks)*

2 When you take the loop out of the bubble mixture and look at it carefully, what do you see? *(4 marks)*

3 What happens when you blow steadily through the loop after it has been dipped in the mixture? *(3 marks)*

4 What is inside a bubble? *(4 marks)*

The slippers that talked

Michelle had never met her Canadian auntie, but she usually sent rather special and unusual presents at Christmas and on birthdays.

"It'll be something good!"

It wasn't. It was a pair of slippers. It was a boring old pair of ordinary, every-day bedroom slippers. All right, so one was red and one was blue, and each one had a funny face on it, but who wants bedroom slippers for a seventh birthday present? Not Michelle, that's for sure.

"I don't feel very well," said Michelle, who was suddenly feeling sick all over again.

"Now don't worry," said Mum, "you just lie back and rest. Look, I've put a bowl on the floor here if you want to be sick. And if you need me, you just shout. OK?"

"OK," said Michelle, who wasn't feeling at all OK.

"Just get as much rest as you can," said Mum, as she made her way downstairs.

"That's it, as much rest as you can," said Dad, as he followed Mum out of the room.

"Bother!" said Michelle when her parents had gone. "Bother!" And she picked up the slippers and threw them on to the floor.

"Ouch!" said one slipper.

"Ouch!" said the other.

"What do you mean 'ouch'?" said Michelle.

"I mean, that hurt!" said one of the slippers.

"Are you talking to me?" Michelle asked, leaning over the edge of her bed and trying to take a closer look at the slippers.

"Yes, of course I am, silly," said the blue slipper.

"Don't you call me silly," said Michelle.

"Well, you called us boring, didn't you?" said the red slipper.

"Well, slippers are boring," said Michelle.

"Ordinary slippers might be boring," said the blue slipper, "but we're not."

Gyles Brandreth from *The Slippers That Talked* (Puffin)

 Choose the correct answer to each question and write it out. *(3 marks each)*

1 Why did Mum put a bowl by Michelle's bed?

   a) She put a bowl there so that Michelle could have a wash.
   b) She put a bowl there in case Michelle was sick.

2 How old was Michelle?

   a) Michelle was nearly eight.
   b) Michelle was just seven.

3 Who sent Michelle the slippers?

   a) Michelle's auntie sent the slippers.
   b) Michelle's mother sent the slippers.

4 What could the slippers do?

   a) The slippers could walk.
   b) The slippers could talk.

5 What colour were the slippers?

   a) One slipper was red and one slipper was blue.
   b) The slippers were red with blue faces on them.

UNIT 18

Fan the fish

Write out the sentences in the correct order to explain how to play **"Fan the fish"**. *(15 marks)*

Then have a race with your friends by using the newspapers to fan the fish along the floor.

Get ready for the game by drawing some big fat fish on newspaper and cutting them out.

Give each friend a cut-out fish and a folded newspaper.

The carwash

Once there was a boy called Lenny. He lived in a part of London so ordinary nobody ever noticed it. Nobody ever noticed Lenny, either. He had ordinary freckles and ordinary hair and his grin was an ordinary grin.

Only one thing made Lenny special. He wanted a carwash for Christmas.

"A what?" asked his Dad.

"A carwash," said Lenny.

"They don't make them, son. Toy cars - yes. Or toy garages. But not a toy carwash."

"I don't want a *toy* carwash, Dad. I want a *real* one."

"A *real* carwash? What, up here in the flat?"

"We could put it out on the balcony," said Lenny, hopefully.

His Dad laughed and so did his Mum.

"What about a cowboy-outfit?" they suggested.

"Or a computer? Or a football game?"

"Thanks," said Lenny. "I'll have one of those instead."

He said this because he didn't want to disappoint his Mum and Dad. Really, he wanted a carwash all the time.

"Why a carwash?" asked his Gran.

"I just like them," Lenny said. ⇨

33

First the money goes clink in the slot and the carwash goes clunk all over. Then comes a spatter of water and a buzz of machinery. The brushes begin to turn. They look like giant spiders turning head-over-heels.

Help!

Are they creeping up on the car or is the car creeping up on them?

More water comes next. It pitter-patters on the bonnet and windscreen and side-windows and roof till the brushes catch up. After this comes a storm of spidery bristles pressing flat against the glass while the car shudders.

Suddenly it all stops.

And starts again just as suddenly. It's the same only backwards – pitter-patter and bristles, bristles and pitter-patter.

Too soon the carwash clunks to a halt. The car drips and glistens ...

"You really do want a carwash for Christmas," said Gran. "I can tell by your face."

Chris Powling from *The Phantom Carwash* (Heinemann)

Choose the correct answer to each question and write it out. *(2 marks each + 1 bonus mark for answering all)*

1   What kind of carwash did Lenny want for Christmas?

   a) He wanted a toy carwash.

   b) He wanted a real carwash.

2   Where did Lenny live?

   a) Lenny lived in a flat in London.

   b) Lenny lived in a flat near London.

3   Why do you think his parents laughed when he said he could keep the carwash on the balcony?

   a) They laughed because it was a silly idea.

   b) They laughed because Lenny was joking.

4   What did Lenny think the brushes of a carwash looked like?

   a) He thought they looked like giant spiders.

   b) He thought they looked like clowns in a circus.

5   Which word in the passages means "shines"?

   a) "Glistens" means "shines".

   b) "Shudders" means "shines".

6   Why did Lenny pretend he'd like something else (like a computer) for Christmas?

   a) He pretended to please his parents.

   b) He pretended because he was a greedy boy.

7   How did Gran know he really wanted a carwash all the time?

   a) She knew because he told her.

   b) She knew by the expression on his face.

UNIT 20

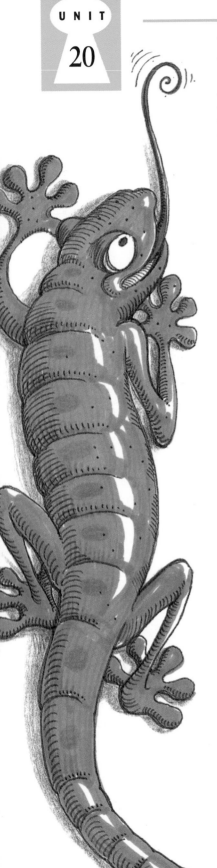

If I were

If I were a lizard
I'd lie around all day
And stick out my tongue
In a very naughty way.

And my mother couldn't tell me
It's a wicked thing to do
Since she would be a lizard
And she would do it too.

If I were a cricket
I'd hop around all day
And suck my teeth quite often
In a chirping sort of way.

And my mother couldn't tell me
It's a wicked thing to do
Since she would be a cricket
And she would do it too.

If I were a rat bat
Then I would sleep all day
And stay awake the livelong night
In a most upsetting way.

And my mother couldn't tell me
It's a wicked thing to do
Since she would be a rat bat
And she would do it too.

If I were an earthworm
I'd play in dirt all day
And drag my feet behind me
In a lazy sort of way.

And my mother couldn't tell me
It's wicked thing to do
Since she would be an earthworm
And she would do it too.

Pamela Mordecai from *New Caribbean Reader 4*
(Ginn & Co)

Answer in sentences.

1   What two things would the boy like doing if he were a lizard? *(4 marks)*

2   If he were a cricket, what would he do? *(3 marks)*

3   Is it true that if he were a rat bat, he would stay awake all day and sleep all night? *(3 marks)*

4   Write down one of the things he would be allowed to do if he were an earthworm. *(2 marks)*

5   What do you find out about the boy's mother in the poem? *(3 marks)*

UNIT
21

Sam's wonderful shell

Sam liked going to Mrs Brown's with Mum. Mum was a home help. She went every day to look after Mrs Brown's house.

She washed the dishes, made the bed, cleaned the floors, and polished the furniture.

Sam liked the house because it wasn't a bit like his own home.

He lived in a high block of flats. There, everything was new and shiny. There weren't nearly as many cupboards or secret places.

But in Mrs Brown's house there were lots of interesting things, and almost everything had a story about it.

There was a row of old china mugs in a cabinet with a glass front. There was a shining silver teapot. There was a small box with medals which Mrs Brown's husband had won when he was a soldier.

But best of all, there was the shell.

"I got this at the seaside when I was little – oh, just five years old. It came from Scotland. Hold it to your ear. Now listen. If you listen very carefully, you can hear the sea."

Sam put it to his ear and listened. Sure enough he could hear the sea roaring in the distance.

Anne Forsyth from *Sam's Wonderful Shell* (Hamish Hamilton)

Answer in sentences.

1   How often did Sam's mother go to Mrs Brown's house? *(2 marks)*

2   Make a list of the jobs that Sam's mother did for Mrs Brown.
    (4 marks)

3   How old was Mrs Brown when she got the shell? *(2 marks)*

4   Is it true that Sam's house was just like Mrs Brown's? *(2 marks)*

5   Why do you think that Sam thought the shell was wonderful?
    (3 marks)

6   Why do you think Mrs Brown needed a home help? *(2 marks)*

UNIT 22

A shaggy dog story

Timmy sat on the back step and watched Ginger. The cat washed first one paw and then the other. Timmy sighed. He loved Ginger very much but he did so want a dog.

"You see, a dog will run after a ball or fetch a stick," he told Ginger. "Cats don't do that."

He wondered if Ginger would fetch something. After all, he was a very special cat. Timmy picked up a twig and threw it down the garden. Ginger ignored it and began to wash the tip of his tail.

"Just as I thought!" Timmy said, sadly. "Dogs are different. You can take dogs for walks, and give them baths and teach them tricks."

Ginger yawned to show that he thought dogs were boring.

"It doesn't have to be a big dog," Timmy went on. "A little dog would do."

He went into the kitchen where Dad was peeling some potatoes.

"Are you sure I can't have a dog?" Timmy asked.

Dad smiled. "No, no, a thousand times no!" he said. "I've told you before, dogs cost money. They have to be fed and if they get ill you have to call in the vet. We can't afford vet's bills. But cheer up, Timmy. You've got Ginger, remember."

"But he's not a dog," Timmy muttered, so Dad couldn't hear.

Pamela Oldfield from *A Shaggy Dog Story*
(Blackie Children's Books)

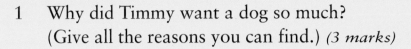 **Answer in sentences.**

1   Why did Timmy want a dog so much?
(Give all the reasons you can find.) *(3 marks)*

2   We can tell that Timmy has asked his father before for a dog.
Which words tell us this? *(2 marks)*

3   What were Dad's reasons for not letting Timmy have a dog?
(4 marks)

4   Do you think the reasons Dad gave Timmy were good reasons
for not having a dog? Why? *(2 marks)*

5   How did Timmy feel at the end of the passage? *(1 mark)*

6   Why do you think Timmy's cat was called Ginger? *(1 mark)*

7   "When Timmy picked up a twig and threw it down the garden,
his cat ignored it."
What words could you use instead of "ignored"? *(2 marks)*

UNIT 23

The owl who was afraid of the dark

Plop was afraid of the dark.

"You *can't* be afraid of the dark," said his Mummy. "Owls are *never* afraid of the dark."

"This one is," Plop said.

"But owls are *night* birds," she said.

Plop looked down at his toes. "I don't want to be a night bird," he mumbled. "I want to be a day bird."

"You *are* what you *are*," said Mrs Barn Owl firmly.

"Yes, I know," agreed Plop, "and what I are is afraid of the dark."

"Oh dear," said Mrs Barn Owl.

It was clear that she was going to need a lot of patience. She shut her eyes and tried to think how best she could help Plop not be afraid. Plop waited.

His mother opened her eyes again. "Plop, you are only afraid of the dark because you don't know about it. What *do* you know about the dark?"

"It's black," said Plop.

"Well, that's wrong for a start. It can be silver or blue or grey or lots of other colours, but almost never black. What else do you know about it?"

"I don't like it," said Plop. "I do not like it AT ALL."

"That's not *knowing* something," said his mother. "That's *feeling* something. I don't think you know anything about the dark at all."

"Dark is nasty," Plop said loudly.

Jill Tomlinson from *The Owl Who Was Afraid of the Dark* (Egmont)

Choose the correct answer to each question and write it out. *(3 marks each)*

1 What do night birds do at night?

   a) Night birds hunt for food at night.
   b) Night birds sleep at night.

2 How did Mrs Barn Owl feel when she heard that Plop was afraid of the dark?

   a) Mrs Barn Owl felt very pleased.
   b) Mrs Barn Owl felt very worried.

3 What did Mrs Barn Owl mean when she said to Plop, "You *are* what you *are*"?

   a) She meant that Plop was a very silly bird.
   b) She meant that Plop couldn't stop being a night bird.

4 Mrs Barn Owl thought that she was going to need a lot of patience. What does this mean?

   a) It means that she would have to try not to get angry.
   b) It means that she would have to eat a lot very soon.

5 Why did Mrs Barn Owl shut her eyes?

   a) Mrs Barn Owl shut her eyes because she was very tired and wanted to sleep.
   b) Mrs Barn Owl shut her eyes so that she could think.

UNIT 24

The awful birthday present

It had been James's birthday the day before, and Grandpa Briggs had given him a watch. It had a second hand and James was very proud of it.

"If you ask me, Grandpa Briggs has more money than sense," said Auntie Lizzie. "There's a parcel for you on the table. I expect you thought I'd forgotten."

James really hoped she *had* forgotten. Last year she had knitted him a pink woolly hat with a red tassel on it. The year before it had been green and pink striped socks. Perhaps she would have used up all the pink wool by now. He hoped so.

The parcel was wrapped in a piece of wallpaper left over from Auntie Lizzie's decorating. It was tied with green string.

James opened the parcel slowly. It was worse than he expected. It was something knitted in green, orange and blue wool. He lifted it and held it up.

It was a jumper with a round neck. At least the neck was supposed to be round but it was all sort of wobbly.

"Try it on, then," said Auntie Lizzie.

James slipped the jumper over his head. The arms were too long and the body was too short. Auntie Lizzie beamed.

"I made a good job of that, I must say," she said. "Don't you look smart?"

James looked at himself in the mirror. He thought he looked awful.

Minna Taylor from *The Awful Birthday Present* (Hodder Children's Books)

🔑⚏ Answer in sentences.

1   What had Grandpa Briggs given James for his birthday? *(2 marks)*

2   What did Auntie Lizzie think of the present Grandpa Briggs
    had given James? *(3 marks)*

3   Why did James hope that Auntie Lizzie had forgotten to
    give him a present? *(3 marks)*

4   Describe how Auntie Lizzie had wrapped James's present. *(2 marks)*

5   How do you know that James did not look smart in the
    jumper that Auntie Lizzie had knitted for him? *(3 marks)*

6   Why did Auntie Lizzie beam when she saw James in
    the jumper? *(2 marks)*

UNIT 25

Lion at school

Once upon a time there was a little girl who didn't like going to school. She always set off late. Then she had to hurry, but she never hurried fast enough.

One morning she was hurrying along as usual when she turned a corner and there stood a lion, blocking her way. He stood waiting for her. He stared at her with his yellow eyes. He growled, and when he growled the little girl could see that his teeth were as sharp as skewers and knives. He growled: "I'm going to eat you up."

"Oh dear!" said the little girl, and she began to cry.

"Wait!" said the lion. "I haven't finished. I'm going to eat you up UNLESS you take me to school with you."

"Oh dear!" said the little girl. "I couldn't do that. My teacher says we mustn't bring pets to school."

"I'm not a pet," said the lion. He growled again and she saw that his tail swished from side to side in anger – *swish! swash!* "You can tell your teacher that I'm a friend who is coming to school with you," he said. "Now shall we go?"

The little girl had stopped crying. She said: "All right. But you must promise two things. First of all, you mustn't eat anyone: it's not allowed."

"I suppose I can growl?" said the lion.

"I suppose you can," said the little girl.

"And I suppose I can roar?"

"Must you?" said the little girl.

"Yes," said the lion.

"Then I suppose you can," said the little girl.

"And what's the second thing?" asked the lion.

"You must let me ride on your back to school."

"Very well," said the lion. He crouched down on the pavement and the little girl climbed on to his back. She held on by his mane. Then they went on together towards the school, the little girl riding the lion. The lion ran with the little girl on his back to school. Even so, they were late. The little girl and the lion went into the classroom just as the teacher was calling the register.

The teacher stopped calling the register when she saw the little girl and the lion. She stared at the lion, and all the other children stared at the lion, wondering what the teacher was going to say. The teacher said to the little girl: "You know you are not allowed to bring pets to school."

The lion began to swish his tail – *swish! swash!* The little girl said: "This is not a pet. This is my friend who is coming to school with me."

The teacher still stared at the lion, but she said to the little girl: "What is his name, then?"

"Noil," said the little girl. "His name is Noil. Just Noil." She knew it would be no good to tell the teacher that her friend was a lion, so she had turned his name backwards: LION – NOIL.

The teacher wrote the name down in the register: NOIL. Then she finished calling the register.

"Betty Small," she said.

"Yes," said the little girl.

"Noil," said the teacher.

"Yes," said the lion. He mumbled, opening his mouth as little as possible, so that the teacher should not see his teeth as sharp as skewers and knives. ⇨

Philippa Pearce from *Lion at School and Other Stories* (Puffin)

Choose the correct answer to each question and write it out.

1   What colour were the lion's eyes? *(2 marks)*

   a) His eyes were red.
   b) His eyes were yellow.

2   What did the lion do when he was angry? *(2 marks)*

   a) He swished his tail.
   b) He closed his eyes.

3   What did the lion say he would do if the little girl wouldn't take him to school? *(2 marks)*

   a) He would eat her up.
   b) He would eat her teacher up.

4   What was the little girl's name? *(1 mark)*

   a) Her name was Noil.
   b) Her name was Betty.

5   What do we know about the lion's teeth? *(2 marks)*

   a) We know they were not sharp.
   b) We know they were sharp.

6   What was the teacher doing when they got to school? *(2 marks)*

   a) The teacher was shouting at the children.
   b) The teacher was checking who had come to school.

7   Why did the lion mumble when he talked to the teacher? *(2 marks)*

   a) The lion didn't want to show his teeth.
   b) The lion couldn't talk very well.

8   What did the lion do to help the little girl to get on to his back? *(2 marks)*

   a) He bent down low so she could climb on.
   b) He sat down so she could climb on.

Index from *Book of Famous Women*

Keller, Helen (1880–1968)
   blind and deaf 50, 52, 55, 62
   birth, USA 49
   Braille 58
   Sullivan, Annie 56–57, 59, 61
   university 62

Nightingale, Florence (1820-1910)
   birth, Florence, Italy 28
   Crimean War 36–38
   "lady with the lamp" 37
   message from God 31
   nursing 32, 34, 35–38, 39

Parks, Rosa (1913–)
   arrest 70–71
   birth, USA 66
   civil rights movement
     71, 75, 77-78
   Martin Luther King 78, 80
   segregation 71, 75, 77

Pocahontas (1595–1617)
   birth, USA 12
   Captain John Smith 14–15
   illness 21
   visit to England 18–20

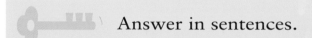

Answer in sentences.

1   Where in a book would you find the index? *(2 marks)*

2   Why do you think Florence Nightingale was called Florence?
   (3 marks)

3   Which of the women was the youngest when she died? *(2 marks)*

4   Which of these women comes first in the book itself? (Look at the
   page numbers!) *(3 marks)*

5   On which pages could you look to find information about Annie
   Sullivan? *(2 marks)*

6   What would you read about on pages 12, 28, 49 and 66? *(3 marks)*

Wheels

Wheels are a familiar part of our everyday life in the twenty-first century. They are so familiar that we tend to take them for granted. However, they are probably the most important invention that has ever been made.

The very first wheels, nearly 5000 years ago, were slices of tree trunks. Wheels have come a long way since then. Wheels today are made of metal and are fitted with rubber tyres filled with air. A wheel does not have to be heavy to be strong. Indeed, one top-of-the-range aluminium front wheel for a racing cycle weighs only 722 grams – a lot less than a 1-kilogram bag of sugar!

We see wheels everywhere: on buses and coaches, cars, vans and lorries, bicycles and motor bicycles, tractors and aeroplanes. Some of our suitcases even have wheels attached so that we don't have to carry them.

Without wheels our lives would be very different. Heavy loads would have to be dragged along the ground; if we wanted to travel any distance, we would have either to walk all the way or ride on the back of a horse or donkey. With wheels, all that is changed.

The simple idea of a pair of wheels fixed firmly to an axle has made modern transport possible. The wheels are helped by ball bearings to turn easily and smoothly when the engine is started, and modern tyres make contact with the road comfortable and bouncy. Travel becomes available for all, and goods can be moved around the country to shops and supermarkets.

The wheel has indeed made possible much of what we take for granted today.

Choose the correct answer to each question and write it out.

1   What century are we living in? *(1 mark)*
    a) We are living in the twentieth century.
    b) We are living in the twenty-first century.

2   What does "we take something for granted" mean? *(2 marks)*
    a) It means that we don't bother to think how important it is.
    b) It means that we pay a lot of money for it.

3   What were the earliest wheels made of? *(2 marks)*
    a) The earliest wheels were made of wood.
    b) The earliest wheels were made of metal.

4   What does "top-of-the-range" mean?   *(2 marks)*
    a) It means that it is very large.
    b) It means that it is the very best that you can buy.

5   How long ago was the first wheel invented? *(2 marks)*
    a) The first wheel was invented about 50,000 years ago.
    b) The first wheel was invented about 5000 years ago.

6   How did people travel before wheels were invented? *(2 marks)*
    a) They caught an old-fashioned bus.
    b) They walked, or rode on a horse or donkey.

7   What do ball bearings help to do? *(2 marks)*
    a) The ball bearings help the axle to turn more easily.
    b) The ball bearings help the wheels to turn more easily.

8   What does it mean when we say "wheels have come a long way"? *(2 marks)*
    a) It means that wheels have travelled millions of miles.
    b) It means that wheels have been greatly improved over the
       centuries.

UNIT 28

Learning about each other

I am lucky to be in a school
with many different cultures.
I get on quite well with the
dark coloured girls in this
class. And some of the English
children are friendly and kind
to me and Hao. But some call
us names because we are
Chinese. But I don't care.
I am proud to be Chinese.
I am proud of my language.
Why don't we all learn about
each other and get on as
friends?

Hanh Tat (Vietnam and UK) from *Rainbow World:*
Poems from Many Cultures, edited by Debjani Chatterjee
and Bashabi Fraser (Hodder Wayland)

Write out the five sentences that are true.
(3 marks each)

1   Hanh Tat is angry in this poem.

2   Hanh Tat is proud of being Chinese.

3   The poet thinks it would be best if everyone stayed in their own group.

4   Hanh Tat wishes all the children in her class were Chinese.

5   Hao is Chinese.

6   The shortest sentence in this poem has four words in it.

7   All the English children in the class are kind to Hanh Tat.

8   Some children in the class call Hanh Tat names because she is Chinese.

9   The poem finishes with a question.

UNIT 29 Ideas for poems

Grace Nichols

When I was a little girl in Guyana we didn't have television (though Guyana has television now), so people had to find their own enjoyment. Our house was always full of friends who would visit us at night, sometimes just to talk stories. I would love being in the midst of everything. When they started to tell jumbie stories (ghost stories) there I'd be sitting, hanging on to every word, feeling the goose pimples on my skin.

I Like to Stay Up

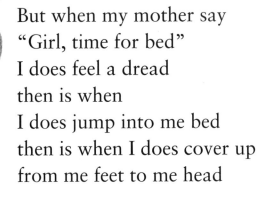

I like to stay up
and listen
when big people talking
jumbie stories

OoooooooooooH
I does feel so tingly
and excited
inside me

But when my mother say
"Girl, time for bed"
I does feel a dread
then is when
I does jump into me bed
then is when I does cover up
from me feet to me head

then is when
I does wish
I didn't listen
to no stupid jumbie story
then is when
I does wish
I did read me book instead

Of course, a poet doesn't only get ideas for poems from childhood, or is only inspired by that. Ideas for poems come from all about, sometimes when you least expect them to.

Sometimes you get ideas from what people say. I got an idea for a poem this way. I was having a chat with a friend of mine and she was telling me something about her little nephew called Peter, who she said loved bananas. One day he was sitting at the table when he suddenly banged his spoon and announced, "I'm a banana man," because his mother had given him something to eat that he didn't like.

That line, "I'm a banana man" immediately started to jump around in my head. What a lovely line I thought. "I'm a banana man, I'm a banana man." Sometimes when you get an idea for a poem in your head, it keeps haunting you. Some ideas are more pushy than others. This idea just kept buzzing around in my head saying please, please write me. I just had to sit down as soon as I got home and write the poem 'I'm a Banana Man' for Peter. As I was writing this poem I was saying it aloud. I think poems, especially poems for children, should not only be read on the page but should be said out aloud too, to hear and taste all the sounds and rhythms in the poem.

I'm a Banana Man

I'm a banana man
I just love shaking
those yellow hands
yes man

Banana in the morning
Banana in the evening
Banana before I go to bed
at night, that's right
that's how much I love
the Banana Bite

I'm a banana man
not a Superman
or a Batman
or a Spiderman
no man

Banana in the morning
Banana in the evening
Banana before I go to bed
at night, that's right
that's how much I love
the Banana bite

Grace Nichols from 'No television but a
lot of friends' in *There's a Poet Behind You*,
edited by Morag Styles and Helen Cook
(A & C Black)

Answer in sentences.

1   Read the verse in the first poem again beginning with "OooooooooooH". Why does Grace Nichols spell it like this?
    (3 marks)

2   Read verse 3 again, the one beginning "But when my mother say…". Find two words in this verse that rhyme with "bed".
    (1 mark)

3   Who told Grace Nichols that Peter said he was a banana man?
    (2 marks)

4   What did Peter mean when he said that he was a banana man?
    (2 marks)

5   Grace Nichols says that the idea for the poem "haunted" her. How can an idea haunt you? *(3 marks)*

6   What can you enjoy more about the two poems here if you say them aloud?*(3 marks)*

7   There are four verses in "I'm a Banana Man". Which two verses are exactly the same? *(1 mark)*
    a) verses 1 and 3
    b) verses 2 and 3
    c) verses 2 and 4
    d) verses 1 and 4

UNIT 30

Sold out

Louisa, nicknamed Weezer, and her sister, Annie, are on their way to buy tickets for the ballet, "Coppélia".

Weezer spent the whole of the bus ride from our house to the theatre telling me the story of "Coppélia". She came tearing back from her ballet class at lunchtime and could hardly eat anything at all because she was so excited.

So there we were on the bus and Weezer was talking, and I wasn't really listening to her properly. I was staring out of the window and pieces of the story floated into my ears from time to time.

"A spooky doctor who makes a doll … his name is Coppélius, so the doll's called Coppélia … she's so real that the hero, Fritz, falls in love with her … but Fritz's girlfriend, Swanilda, plays a trick on him … she dresses up in the doll's clothes and the Doctor thinks it's real magic and she's come alive … it all ends happily, though. When you see it, it'll all be much clearer. The music's lovely. Are we nearly there?"

"Yes," I said. "Come on, we're getting off now."

"Yippee!" Weezer said and everyone on the bus turned to look at us. "I don't care," she whispered to me. "I'm going to get tickets for the ballet."

The Theatre Royal had thick red carpets in the foyer.

"There," said Weezer. "That's the Box Office."

"It looks more like a cage than a box," I said. "Look at the gold bars. The ladies who work there must feel as though they're in a zoo or something."

Weezer giggled. "We could feed them bananas through the bars."

"Ssh!" I said. "Behave yourself. I'm going to queue up now."

We had to wait about ten minutes until it was our turn.

"Yes, dear?" said the lady behind the bars. "What can I do for you?"

"I'd like two tickets for "Coppélia" for next Saturday's matinée, please," I said.

"It's sold out, I'm afraid," said the lady.

"Sold out? What does that mean?"

"We have no more tickets for the Russian Ballet left at all. Every single performance has been sold out since last week. I'm very sorry."

Adèle Geras from *Louisa in the Wings* (Red Fox)

Answer in sentences.

1   How do you think that Louisa might have got her nickname?
    (2 marks)

2   Annie doesn't listen properly when Weezer is telling her the story of "Coppélia". How does the author show us that she hears only little bits here and there? *(2 marks)*

3   In the story of the ballet, what trick does Swanilda play on Fritz?
    (2 marks)

4   Weezer tells Annie that the story ends happily in the end. What do you think will make Swanilda happy? *(2 marks)*

5   How can you tell that Weezer is mad about ballet? Mention as many clues as you can. *(5 marks)*

6   Which two of these words best describe how Weezer felt when she heard that all the tickets had been sold and there were none left?
    relieved   happy   miserable   grateful   sad *(2 marks)*

UNIT

31

How can we stop our world getting warmer?

To understand why the Earth is warming up, you need to understand why it is warm in the first place. Our planet is surrounded by a thick layer of gases called the atmosphere. Sunlight passes through the atmosphere and strikes the Earth. The Sun's rays heat up the Earth's surface. The heat rises into the air. Some of the gases in the atmosphere, including carbon dioxide and methane, trap the heat and reflect it back to Earth. This keeps our planet warm.

Power stations and cars release tonnes of greenhouse gases every day. So you can help stop global warming by using less electricity and by finding ways of getting about other than by car. Ride a bicycle or walk instead of going by car. Turn off lights when you leave a room. Ask your parents to turn down the heating in your house to conserve energy.

Another way to help halt global warming is to plant and care for trees. Because trees take in carbon dioxide, they are our natural allies in the fight against global warming.

The problem of global warming cannot be solved in a day. It may take a long time to find clean sources of energy, such as wind energy, to replace fossil fuels. It may take a long time to replant the trees we are cutting down. But every little thing each person can do to conserve energy and to save our forests will help. Think about our planet. Think about ways you can help make the Earth a safe and comfortable place for the future.

From *Is Our Planet Warming Up?* edited by Elizabeth Kaplan (Heinemann)

 Answer in sentences.

1   What are two of the ways we can save electricity at home? *(2 marks)*

2   How does it help stop global warming if we walk or cycle instead of going by car? *(2 marks)*

3   How do trees help to stop global warming? *(2 marks)*

4   Trees are our allies. What word can you think of that is the opposite of "allies"? *(1 mark)*

5   To conserve energy means to _____ energy. *(2 marks)*

6   Why is wind energy described as clean energy? *(2 marks)*

7   To halt global warming means to _____ it. *(2 marks)*

8   Why is it important to save the world from getting any warmer? *(2 marks)*

UNIT
32

Gulnara the Brave

This story takes place hundreds of years ago in a country called Mongolia. A 'ger' is the word for a special kind of tent. 'Khan' is the word for the ruler or emperor. A 'league' is an old-fashioned word meaning about three miles long.

Gulnara and her sisters lived in a *ger* on the Mongolian plain with their father and one chestnut horse. One day, a messenger ordered the men out to fight in the Khan's army. Gulnara's father wrung his hands, "I'm an old man. I'd be no use".

"Too bad!" declared the messenger. "An order is an order. Obey, or the Khan's men will slit your throat."

"Don't worry, father!" cried his eldest daughter. "I will go in your place." She took her father's bow and sword, jumped on the chestnut's back, and galloped off. She rode until she came to the Iron Mountain. Blocking her way was an evil black fox with a tail three leagues long. The chestnut reared in terror and raced back home.

"Let me go, father!" said the second daughter. She took up the bow and sword, leapt upon the chestnut, and galloped off. She came to the Iron Mountain. Blocking her way was a huge wolf, with a tail three leagues long. The chestnut horse reared with fright and galloped home.

Father wailed. "This isn't woman's work. If I don't go, the Khan's men will slit my throat."

Gulnara stepped forward. "I am the youngest, but I am taller and stronger than my sisters. I'm sure I'll get across the Iron Mountain." With bow and sword, Gulnara jumped onto the chestnut and galloped off. The Iron Mountain rose before her. Blocking the track was a